Theory of Music Exams

GRADE 1

2011

Theory Paper Grade 1   2011   A

TOTAL MARKS
100

Duration 1½ hours

Candidates should answer ALL questions.
Write your answers on this paper – no others will be accepted.
Answers must be written clearly and neatly – otherwise marks may be lost.

1 Add the missing bar-lines to these two melodies. The first bar-line is given in each.

10

2 Write a two-bar rhythm as an answer to the given rhythm.

10

3 Write the tonic triads named below, using the correct key signature for each.

10

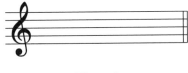

D major   G major

4 (a) Draw a circle around the *higher* note of each of these pairs of notes.

10

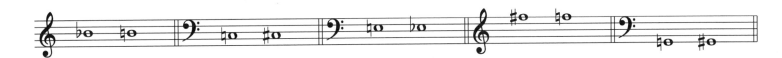

(b) Draw a circle around the *lower* note of each of these pairs of notes.

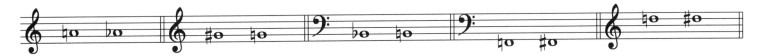

5 (a) Give the letter name of each of the notes marked ✱, including the sharp or f
where necessary. The first answer is given.

A
....

(b) Draw a circle around two notes next to each other that are a 3rd apart.

6 Add the correct clef and any necessary sharp or flat signs to make each of the scales [10]
named below. Do *not* use key signatures.

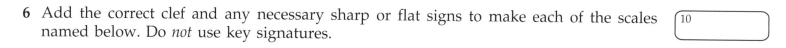

F major

D major

7 Add a rest at the places marked ✱ in these two melodies to make each bar complete. [10]

Donizetti

Tchaikovsky

8 Look at this melody by N. Piccinni and then answer the questions below.

Write your answer to question (c) on the stave below.

(a) Give the meaning of each of these:

    Allegro ....

    mf ....

    ⌒ (e.g. bar 2) ....

    ◁ (bar 7) ....

    > (bar 8) ....

〔10〕

(b) (i)   Give the letter name of the first note in bar 6. ....

    (ii)   This melody is in the key of F major. Draw a circle around a note
          which is the 2nd degree of the scale.

    (iii) How many bars contain a quaver (eighth-note) rest? ....

    (iv) Answer TRUE or FALSE to this sentence:
          The **4** in $\frac{2}{4}$ means crotchet (quarter-note) beats. ....

    (v)   Give the time name (e.g. crotchet or
          quarter note) of the *shortest* note in the melody. ....

〔10〕

(c) Copy out the music from the start of the melody to the end of bar 4, exactly as it is
written above. Don't forget the clef, key signature, time signature, tempo marking,
dynamic and all other details. Write the music on the blank stave above question (a).
(Marks will be given for neatness and accuracy.)

〔10〕

Theory Paper Grade 1   2011   B

TOTAL MARKS
100

Duration 1½ hours

Candidates should answer ALL questions.
Write your answers on this paper – no others will be accepted.
Answers must be written clearly and neatly – otherwise marks may be lost.

1 Add the missing bar-lines to these two melodies. The first bar-line is given in each.

10

2 Write a two-bar rhythm as an answer to the given rhythm.

10

3 (a) Add the correct clef to each of these tonic triads.

10

G major   C major

Letter names   ....

(b) Under each triad write the letter name of each of the notes.

4 (a) Name the degree of the scale (e.g. 2nd, 3rd, 4th) of each of the notes marked ✷, as shown in the first answer. The key is F major.

N. Piccinni

2nd

....

(b) Give the time name (e.g. quaver or eighth note) of the rest in the last bar of the melody.

....

5 Add a rest at the places marked ✷ in these two melodies to make each bar complete.

Verdi

Handel

6 Name the key of each of these scales. Also draw a bracket (⌐────┐) over each pair of notes making a semitone, as shown in the first scale.

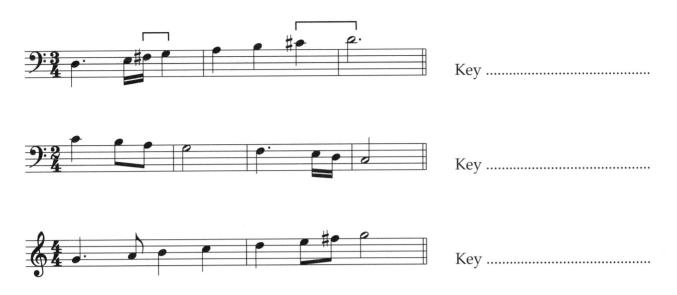

Key ....

Key ....

Key ....

7 *After* each note write a higher note to form the named *melodic* interval, as shown in the first answer. The key is F major.

7th

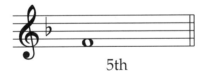

5th

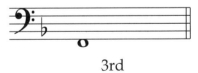

3rd

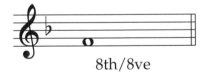

8th/8ve

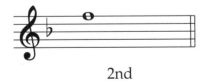

2nd

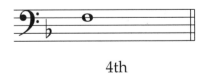

4th

8 Look at this folksong melody and then answer the questions below.

Write your answer to question (c) on the stave below.

(a) Give the meaning of each of these:

Moderato ....

mf ....

the dots above the notes (bar 3) ....

cresc. (bar 3) ....

> (bar 4) ....

[10]

(b) (i) This melody is in the key of D major. Draw a bracket (⌐‾‾‾⌐) over three notes next to each other that make the tonic triad of this key.

[10]

(ii) In which bar is the performer told to pause or hold on to the note? Bar ....

(iii) Draw a circle around a note that you think will sound the *quietest*.

(iv) Give the letter name of the *highest* note in the melody. ....

(v) Give the time name (e.g. crotchet or quarter note) of the *longest* note in the melody. ....

(c) Copy out the music from the start of the melody to the end of bar 4, exactly as it is written above. Don't forget the clef, key signature, time signature, tempo marking, dynamics and all other details. Write the music on the blank stave above question (a). (Marks will be given for neatness and accuracy.)

[10]

Theory Paper Grade 1   2011   C

Duration 1½ hours

Candidates should answer ALL questions.
Write your answers on this paper – no others will be accepted.
Answers must be written clearly and neatly – otherwise marks may be lost.

TOTAL MARKS
100

1   (a)   Add the time signature to each of these three melodies.

10

(b)   Add the missing bar-lines to this melody. The first bar-line is given.

2   Write a two-bar rhythm as an answer to the given rhythm.

10

3 Write as semibreves (whole notes) the scales named below, using the correct key signature for each. [10]

G major, descending

F major, ascending

4 Next to each rest write a note that has the same time value, as shown in the first answer. [10]

5 Give the number (e.g. 2nd, 3rd, 4th) of each of these melodic intervals, as shown in the first answer. The key is D major. [10]

6th

....

....

....

....

....

....

6 **(a)** Give the letter name of each of the notes marked ∗, including the sharp or flat sign where necessary. The first answer is given. ⎡10⎤

Mozart

F♯

....

(b) How many semiquavers (16th notes) is the first note of the last bar (marked ↓) worth in total? ....

7 **(a)** Add the correct clef to each of these tonic triads. ⎡10⎤

C major

G major

Letter names ....

(b) Under each triad write the letter name of each of the notes.

8 Look at this folksong melody and then answer the questions below.

Write your answer to question (c) on the stave below.

(a) Give the meaning of each of these:

10

Adagio ....

mp ....

cantabile ....

rall. (bar 8) ....

dim. (bar 8) ....

(b) (i) Give the time name (e.g. crotchet or
quarter note) of the *longest rest* in the melody. ....

10

(ii) Complete this sentence:
Bars 1 and 2 have the same notes and rhythm as bars .... and ....

(iii) This melody is in the key of F major. Name the degree of
the scale (e.g. 4th, 5th, 6th) of the first note in bar 2 (marked *). ....

(iv) Give the letter name of the *highest* note in the melody. ....

(v) Underline one of the following words that best describes how you think the
bracketed notes in bar 4 (marked ⌐‾‾‾⌐) should be played:
              legato (smoothly)   or   *staccato* (detached)

(c) Copy out the music from the start of bar 6 to the end of the melody, exactly as it is
written above. Don't forget the clef, key signature, dynamics and all other details.
Write the music on the blank stave above question (a).
(Marks will be given for neatness and accuracy.)

10

Theory Paper Grade 1   2011   S

Duration 1½ hours

TOTAL MARKS
100

Candidates should answer ALL questions.
Write your answers on this paper – no others will be accepted.
Answers must be written clearly and neatly – otherwise marks may be lost.

1 (a) Add the time signature to each of these three melodies.

10

(b) Add the missing bar-lines to this melody. The first bar-line is given.

2 Write a two-bar rhythm as an answer to the given rhythm.

10

3 Add the correct clef to make each of these named notes, as shown in the first answer.

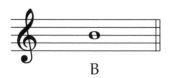
B

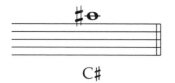
C♯

F

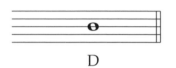
D

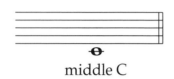
middle C

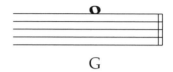
G

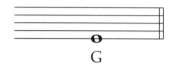
G

A

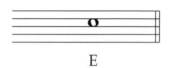
E

F♯

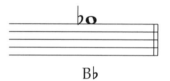
B♭

4 *Above* each note write another note to form the named *harmonic* interval, as shown in the first answer. The key is F major.

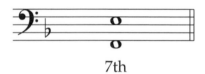
7th

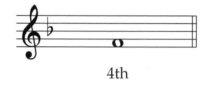
4th

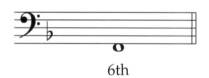
6th

8th/8ve

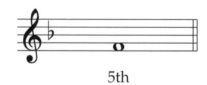
5th

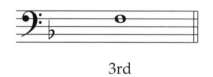
3rd

5 (a) Give the letter name of each of the notes marked ∗, including the sharp or flat sign  where necessary. The first answer is given.

Haydn

C

....

(b) Give the time name (e.g. crotchet or quarter note) of the *first* note of the melody. ....

6 Name the keys of each of these tonic triads, as shown in the first answer.

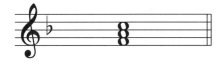

F major
....

....

....

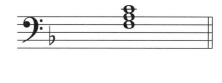

....

....

....

7 Next to each note write a rest that has the same time value, as shown in the first answer.

8 Look at this folksong melody and then answer the questions below.

Write your answer to question (c) on the stave below.

(a) Give the meaning of each of these: 10

Andante ....

cresc. (bar 3) ....

𝆑 (bar 5) ....

rit. (bar 7) ....

⟍ (bars 7–8) ....

(b) (i)   This melody is in the key of G major. Name the degree of   10
            the scale (e.g. 4th, 5th, 6th) of the first note in bar 1 (marked ∗). ....

     (ii)   Give the number of a bar that contains all the
            notes of the tonic triad. Remember the key is G major.   Bar ....

     (iii) Give the time name (e.g. crotchet or
            quarter note) of the *longest* note in the melody. ....

     (iv)   In which bar is the performer asked to accent or force the notes? Bar ....

     (v)   Give the letter name of the *highest* note in the melody. ....

(c) Copy out the music from the start of bar 5 to the end of bar 6, exactly as it is   10
     written above. Don't forget the clef, key signature, dynamics and all other details.
     Write the music on the blank stave above question (a).
     (Marks will be given for neatness and accuracy.)

ABRSM
24 Portland Place
London W1B 1LU
United Kingdom

www.abrsm.org

Theory of Music Exams Model Answers
are also available.

Published by ABRSM (Publishing) Ltd,
a wholly owned subsidiary of ABRSM

Printed in England by Page Bros (Norwich) Ltd

ISBN 978-1-84849-367-4

9 781848 493674